This journal belongs to:

Managing Editor
Mara Ellen Guckian

Editor in Chief
Brent L. Fox, M. Ed.

Creative Director
Sarah M. Fournier

Cover Artist
Kelly McMahon

Art Coordinator
Renée Mc Elwee

Imaging
Amanda R. Harter

Publisher
Mary D. Smith, M.S. Ed.

Edupress
A Division of Teacher Created Resources, Inc.

12621 Western Avenue
Garden Grove, CA 92841
www.teachercreated.com

ISBN: 978-1-4206-0169-5

Reprinted, 2021

Made in U.S.A.

Edupress™
A Division of Teacher Created Resources

Introduction

This book is a journal and it is just for you! All you need to get started are pencils and markers or crayons. Write your name on the first page and add a picture of yourself and your age on page 3.

The rest of the book is filled with spaces to draw and write. On each page you will find a *writing prompt*. Writing prompts are suggestions for you to share things about your life including your memories, your likes and dislikes, your ideas, and your goals. This book can also be a place to share your feelings. What makes you happy? What can make you sad or mad? Sometimes writing or drawing can even make you feel better.

Since this is your very own book, *author* and *illustrator* are two important words to learn:

> The **author** is the person who writes the book—that's you!
>
> The **illustrator** is the person who draws or creates the pictures for a book—you again!

Once you have completed this journal, you should keep it in a special place. That way, you will always have a reminder of your thoughts when you were this age.

Have fun!

Name

I am years old!

Write about your family.

Write about your friends.

Write about your favorite birthday tradition.

Write about a special holiday tradition.

Write about the best part of school.

Write about something you want to learn to do.

Write about something you do every day.

Write about what you like to do outside.

Write about your favorite time of year.

Write about something you wish for.

Write about your favorite trip.

Write about a place you want to go.

Write about what makes you happy ☺.

Write about what you do when you are sad ☹.

Write about something you are thankful for.

Write about a time you were proud.

Write about something that makes you laugh.

Write about your favorite game to play.

What do you like to do on the weekends?

What you would do if you had a tree house?

What would you do with $100?

What do you want to do when you are older?

Imagine you could fly. Where would you go?

Imagine you were invisible. What would you do?

What would you do if you found a baby dinosaur?

What would you do if you found a real magic wand?

Write about an animal you would like to be.

Write about someone you would like to meet.

Name your favorite story. Why do you like it?